Little Miss

G

**Inspired by life with the
Mr. Men and Little Misses**

Illustrated by Adam Hargreaves

A gossip is a person who
is born with a great
sense of rumour.

Mr. Nosey

Don't believe everything you hear.

'Mr. Greedy's put on four stone!'

Then again, it might just be true.

Some people are born to gossip . . .

Mr. Chatterbox

. . . and some people aren't.

Mr. Muddle

Gossip spreads like
Mr. Greedy's stomach.

Mr. Greedy

Sometimes you just know when they are talking about you.

Mr. Quiet

Mr. Noisy is not very
good with secrets.

Walls have ears.

Mr. Nosey

There isn't much point in telling
Mr. Forgetful any gossip.

Mr. Forgetful

Gossip hurts.

Some things are best kept secret.

Little Miss Shy

Private & Confidential
= must be interesting.

Mr. Nosey

gossip/*n*. A person who will never tell a lie . . . if the truth is juicier.

Little Miss Trouble

The nosiest nosey
parker of them all.

Email is the new communication tool for the 21st Century.

Well, it's great for office gossip!

Mr. Chatterbox

Little Miss Chatterbox

If you e-gossip on the e-vine,
e-make e-sure you e-press
the e-right e-button before
you send it!

Nobody tells Mr. Worry any gossip. They think he's got enough to worry about.

Little Miss Chatterbox

Mr. Worry

Gossip always gets back to
the person it's about.

Mr. Mean

Mr. Mean is so mean, he even keeps *gossip* to himself.

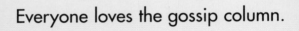

Everyone loves the gossip column.

NEWS

Mr. Tall

Gossip is like a bank account.
The more you put into it,
the more interest you will
get out of it.

Mr. Uppity

Office gossip = facilitating the effici

...stribution of essential workforce data.

Well, it sounds good.

Mr. Perfect

Sadly, no one gossips about people's virtues.

Gossip overload.

Little Miss Curious

Foot in mouth.

Mr. Silly

Idle gossip?

Not if you do it properly.

Mr. Lazy

Global gossip:

French – commerage
Swedish – sladdertacka
Hungarian – pletykalodo
Portuguese – bisbolhetice
Australian – sticky beak

Mr. Clever

Bad news travels fast.
Gossip takes the scenic route.

Little Miss Late

Gossiping over the garden fence was a challenge for Mr. Small.

Mr. Small

Pssst . . . have you heard . . . ?

Mr. Nosey